My
Participate!
Journal

Barnabas
for
Children®

Barnabas for Children® is a registered word mark and the logo is a registered device mark of
The Bible Reading Fellowship.

Published by
The Bible Reading Fellowship
15 The Chambers, Vineyard
Abingdon OX14 3FE
United Kingdom
Tel: +44 (0)1865 319700
Email: enquiries@brf.org.uk
Website: www.brf.org.uk
BRF is a Registered Charity

ISBN 978 1 84101 899 7

First published 2012
10 9 8 7 6 5 4 3 2 1 0

Acknowledgments
Unless otherwise stated, scripture quotations are taken from the Contemporary English Version of the Bible published
by HarperCollins Publishers, copyright © 1991, 1992, 1995 American Bible Society.

Scripture quotations from THE MESSAGE. Copyright © by Eugene H. Peterson 1993, 1994, 1995. Used by permission of
NavPress Publishing Group.

A catalogue record for this book is available from the British Library

Printed in the UK by HSW Print

My
Participate!
Journal

Exploring
what it means to be a
Christian
disciple

Meg Prowting, Penny Fuller & Mike Seaton

Introduction

Welcome to your journal!

This journal is for you to use whenever you want. Decorate it how you like; write your name all over it—anything you want.

After each session of Participate! spend some time in the week trying out the activities in your journal that link with that session.

You can write as much or as little as you like, and you can share your thoughts in your group or keep them to yourself. Your journal is private to you, so you don't have to show it to anyone; you can be as honest as you like. The more you use your journal, the more it will help you to think through the topics that you have begun to discuss in your sessions. If you prefer not to write, you could use colour or drawing, or you could make an electronic journal using a video camera or something similar.

If you want to talk about anything in your journal, speak to your group leader or someone in the church who you know and trust.

Colour wheel

On the inside back cover of your journal, there is a colour wheel. If you get asked a question about how you feel, sometimes it is hard to put the answer into words. The colour wheel helps to describe your feelings in terms of colours. The warm colours—red, orange and yellow—might make us feel warm or hot when we look at them. Warm colours might also make us feel active, energised or excited. The cool colours are green, blue and violet. These colours might make us feel cool, alone, sad or quiet. Think of as many things as you can in nature that are cool colours or make us feel cold. Think of as many things as you can in nature that are warm colours or make us feel warm.

Throughout your journal, there is plenty of opportunity to reflect on what you have experienced. Use your colour wheel to choose a colour that feels right for you at that moment. You could write down how you feel or write down the colour, or you could use the colour in your journal. Think about what colour you were immediately drawn to and how the colour makes you feel.

As the sessions progress, revisit the questions in your journal. Has the colour you originally chose changed? If the answer is yes, why do you think this is?

Who am I?

Find a photo of yourself to stick here. You can decorate this page if you want to.

Remember!

In this session, we explored our identity. We looked at who we are and what the Bible has to say about us as individuals.

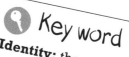
Ask your parents (or people who have known you for a long time) whether you have changed much since you were younger and how you have changed. What did they say?

How did you feel in your group? Did you feel comfortable and confident? If not, why do you think you didn't? (Don't forget to use the colour wheel at the back to help you.)

When did you become 'you'? Was it when you were born or when you were five, eight or ten years old? Or are you still not 'you'? What makes you 'you'?

 # Look it up

The Bible passages in the group session may have included Psalm 139 and Genesis 1:26. You may like to look them up in your own Bible and read them again.

How do the passages make you feel?

Do you like the idea that God made you in his image?

In the session, you may have talked about how people might hide 'the real me'. If you want to, use the space below to write your own poem or song about the 'real you'.

What has the session on identity made you think about?

Don't forget this week's challenge!

Think about how you could influence people in a positive way this week by being yourself.

You may want to chat with God about how he can help you with this challenge. If you want to, use the space below to write or draw your prayer to God.

Use the space below to write about your week, your thoughts about God and how you have been getting on with your challenge.

Valued for who I am

Remember!

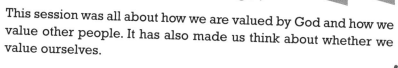

This session was all about how we are valued by God and how we value other people. It has also made us think about whether we value ourselves.

Challenge for the week

Think about how you could make other people feel special and valued this week.

 ## Key word

Value: How important something is to a person.

What do you value the most? How do you show that you value it?

11

 # Look it up

The Bible passages in the group session may have included Matthew 10:29–31 and Luke 19:1–10. You may like to look them up in your own Bible and read them again.

How do the passages make you feel?

In Luke 19:1–10, Jesus chose to go to Zacchaeus' house, even though Zacchaeus was seen by others as an unrespectable thief. What does this tell you about Jesus?

My fingerprint

Fingerprints are unique—no one else in the world has the same fingerprints as you. Try to put a print of one of your fingers in the box opposite to remind you that you are a special and unique person.

What do you like about yourself?
 Use the space below to write or draw. You don't have to write anything—you can just think about it.

Are there parts of your character that you don't like? Perhaps, for example, you have a bad temper?

Are there parts of who you are that you try to hide from others?

How would you like to change in the future?

Read the letter below from God. Write your own name on the dotted line after the word 'Dear', as this letter is for you.

How does the letter from God make you feel? (Don't forget, you can use the colour wheel if it helps.)

Dear ....

I know you inside out and back to front! I made you and love every part of you. You are unique and special and there is no one else like you.

I have plans for you and your future. I am excited that you are learning more about me and I want you to get to know me so much better.

I love you so very much and I will always be here for you, even when you may feel that I am not.

Your heavenly Father
God

What has this session made you think about?

Dear God...

If you were to write a reply to God's letter, what would you write?

Challenge

How could you make other people feel special and valued this week? Think about or write down what you will try to do this week.

If you want to, use this space to write or draw your prayer to God.

Use the space below to write about your week, your thoughts about God and how you have been getting on with your challenge.

Understanding community

►►► Remember!

This session was all about what a community is and what God wants for communities.

 Key word

Community: a group of people who have something in common.

Challenge for the week

Think of an idea for improving one of the communities you belong to, and then give it a go.

Which community do you most enjoy belonging to?

Which community would you most like to belong to?

God changed Abram's name to Abraham (which means 'father of many'). Look up the meaning of your name and write it here.

Do you think it reflects your true character?

You may have looked at the cartoon about the community of Israel in your session. Choose one of the following stories from the cartoon to read in more detail.

- God calls Abram (Genesis 12).
- God tests Abraham (Genesis 22:1–19).
- Joseph's brothers' jealousy (Genesis 37).
- God reveals himself to the community of Israel and gives his people the Ten Commandments (Exodus 20:1–21).

What do you like about this story?

What don't you like, and why?

What problems or difficult situations are there in your local community?

Use this space to write a prayer for the difficult situation.

Which people in the communities you belong to have had a positive influence on your life?

Why do you think they had a positive influence on you?

Your neighbour is anyone who is in the same community as you. Your neighbour could be someone on the other side of the world, because we all belong to a global community. The Bible tells us that we should love our neighbour. Do you find it difficult to love your neighbour? If so, why?

What could you do to make your community a better place and show love to your neighbour?

You might find it useful to look up the website 'We are what we do' (www.wearewhatwedo.org).

What has this session made you think about?

You may want to use the space below to write or draw a prayer to God.

Use the space below to write about your week, your thoughts about God and how you have been getting on with your challenge.

Church as a community of believers

 **Remember!**

This session was all about how church is a community and how we all have a part to play in that community.

🔑 **Key words**

Community: a group of people who have something in common.
Church: a community of Christian believers.

Challenge for the week

Complete the Communities Questionnaire on page 27 of your journal. You'll need to have this with you for Session 6.

 Look it up

The Bible passages in the group session may have included 1 Corinthians 12:12–26 and Ephesians 4:16. You may like to look them up in your own Bible and read them again.

How do the passages make you feel?

1 Corinthians 12:12–26 describes the church as a body and everyone in it as part of the body. If you were to describe yourself as a part of the body of the church, which part would you choose, and why?

How do you feel about going to church? (Don't forget to use the colour wheel if it helps you.)

What do you like most about your church?

What do you like least about your church?

In what ways do you feel part of your church community?

Choose a colour from the colour wheel that best describes how important you feel church is to you.

Use the space below to design your ideal church. Don't just draw the building, but remember to think about what would happen inside the church. What would the people be like? What would you most like to do in your ideal church? Be creative!

How does it make you feel when you hear that some Christians in other parts of the world are treated badly because they go to church?

Use the space below to write a prayer for these people.

Some people feel closest to God when they are at church. Others feel close to God on their own, or outside, or in many different places. Where do you feel closest to God?

Use the space below to write or draw a prayer to God about anything that this session has made you think about.

What has this session made you think about?

Communities Questionnaire

Speak to members of your church and ask them the following questions. Make a note of their answers.

- Where do you work?

- What role do you have?

- What training support do you have for that role?

- How does your faith influence your work?

- Do you meet with other Christians within your work community?

- How does this compare with your church life?

- How would you describe your role within the church?

Use the space below to write about your week, your thoughts about God and how you have been getting on with your challenge.

Hearing God's call

 ## Remember!

In this session we have looked at what it means to be called by God to do something. We learned that all Christians are called to get to know God and do his work.

 ## Key word

Calling: when God asks you to do something. It might come as a feeling, a dream or an inner voice. God can call people in different ways.

 ## Look it up

The Bible passages in the group session may have included the following. Think about some of the stories you have learnt about. You may like to look them up in your own Bible and read them again.

Challenge for the week

Spend some time this week talking and listening to God.

- Moses: Exodus 3:1–12
- Jonah: Jonah 1:1—3:3
- Peter walking on water: Matthew 14:22–31

How do the passages make you feel?

Choose one of the stories. Use this space to write down what questions you have about the story.

Do you find it easy to believe this story? Think about the reasons why you find it easy to believe, or why you find it difficult to believe.

Peter was challenged by Jesus to get out of the boat and walk on the water. He had to step out of his 'comfort zone' to do something he had never done before. (Being in your comfort zone means that you stick to what you know rather than trying something new.)

How would you respond if someone asked you to do something that you had never done before?

If you were Peter, would you have stepped out of the boat on to the water?

Do you think God still talks to people in the way he did in biblical times?

Speak to someone you know well at church. Ask them if they have ever felt called by God to do something.

All Christians are called to get to know God and follow his ways. Do you find it hard or easy to get to know God? (Don't forget, you can use the colour wheel if it helps.)

What practical things could help you to get to know God better and follow his ways?

Have you ever heard God or had an experience of God? If not, would you like to?

Do you feel called to do or try anything in particular?

How would you know if you were being called?

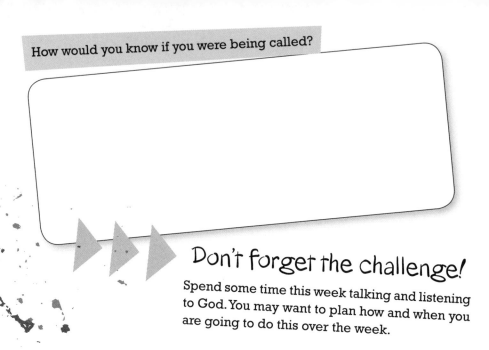

Don't forget the challenge!

Spend some time this week talking and listening to God. You may want to plan how and when you are going to do this over the week.

Use this space to write a prayer to God about anything that this session has made you think about.

What has this session made you think about?

Use the space below to write about your week, your thoughts about God and how you have been getting on with your challenge.

Serving God and others

Remember!

This session was about five key things about what it means to serve God and others.

Challenge for the week

Look carefully to see all the different ways that people serve others in your church and community. See how many ways you can spot!

Key words

Serve: doing something to help others.
God's call: when God asks us to do something.
Response: how we do God's work.
Gifts: qualities given to us by God.
Apostle: a messenger, serving God.
Vocation: a special urge or feeling to try a particular calling or career.

Look it up

The Bible passages in the group session may have included 2 Corinthians 9:12–13. You may like to look up the passage in your own Bible and read it again.

How does the passage make you feel? (Don't forget to use the colour wheel if it helps you.)

When we serve God, our actions not only meet the needs of God's people; they also give thanks to God. When we give freely in order to serve God, other people will praise God because of our generosity in sharing our time and talents with them.

If you were to tell a friend about what it means to serve God, what would you say?

Do you enjoy or dislike serving others?

Write or draw something that shows how your church serves the community.

Do you think your church does enough to help in the community?

Cut stories out of your local newspaper about how people serve in the community. Stick them here.

There are different kinds of spiritual gifts, but they all come from the same Spirit. There are different ways to serve the same Lord, and we can each do different things. Yet the same God works in all of us and helps us in everything we do.

1 CORINTHIANS 12:4–6

How can you share your gifts and talents with others?

If you could volunteer to do anything in your local community or in the world, what would you really like to do? If you are unsure what possibilities there are, you might like to look at leaflets or the internet to see what is possible.

Is there anyone who inspires you, who has served other people?

Think about your gifts and skills. In the list below, draw or stick a smiley face in the boxes that apply to you. Add some of your own ideas to the list.

Skills and gifts	Yes	Yes, but with help	Not sure	Definitely not
I am creative				
I like being active and energetic				
I enjoy talking to people				
I enjoy reading				
I am artistic				
I am good with new technology				
I enjoy looking after people				
I have an interest in my community				
I am interested in the world				
I enjoy debating				
I have patience				
I have good communication skills				
I am good at listening				
I enjoy spending time with my friends				

Skills and gifts	Yes	Yes, but with help	Not sure	Definitely not
I am shy				
I enjoy watching films				
I am interested in nature				
I enjoy computer and console games				
I am good at maths				
I like encouraging other people				
I make people laugh				
I like being active				
I like helping others				
I like drawing				
I enjoy sport				
I can write prayers				
I can sing				
I can play a musical instrument				
I can…				
I like…				
I am…				
I have…				

What do you think is your strongest skill?

Is there a gift/skill that you don't have but that you would particularly like to have?

Use the space below to write a prayer to God about anything that you have thought about during this session.

What has this session made you think about?

Use the space below to write about your week, your thoughts about God and how you have been getting on with your challenge.

Try it!

▶▶▶ Remember!

This session is all about preparing you for your 'Try it!' placement. This is where you get the chance to volunteer to do something for a short time in your church or in your community. You will not be on your own, as you will be working alongside somebody else who normally does that role. Use the questions below during Session 7 with your group to help you prepare for your 'Try it!' placement.

How do I get started?

Think about what you might like to have a go at. What are you interested in trying? It may be something you have always wanted to try, or perhaps it is something you are thinking of volunteering for in the future and you want to see if it is right for you.

Write your thoughts here.

What colour would best describe how you feel about trying something new? (Don't forget to use the colour wheel to help you.)

Note down things that you want to talk with your group leader about. They could be the choices you are thinking of making, or perhaps concerns about not knowing what to choose.

When would you most like to do your placement? It could be midweek, at the weekend, or during the school holidays.

What goals would you like to set to get the best out of your experience? They could be about wanting to learn at least two new skills; they could be about just wanting to have fun. Write down your goals here.

During your session, you will be shown a list of suggested 'Try it!' placements in your church, but you can also research more widely about things you could do in your local community.

Once you have looked at what placements are available with your group, you can make a decision about what you want to try. When you have decided, fill in the information below about your 'Try it!' placement, with the help of your group leader.

Placement details

Name:

My placement is _____

I will be working alongside _____

My placement will take place on _____ (day)

My placement will take place from ____ (time) to ____ (time)

My placement will take place at _____ (place)

The start date of my placement is _____

The finish date of my placement is _____

Other details I need to remember are _____

_____

_____

_____

_____

Use the rest of the questions below to reflect on your own at home, after you have finished the session.

On the colour wheel, what colour best reflects what you knew about yourself at the first session?

What colour best reflects what you know about yourself now?

Is there a difference in your colour choice?

If your answer is yes, why do you think this is?

No test or temptation that comes your way is beyond the course of what others have had to face. All you need to remember is that God will never let you down; he'll never let you be pushed past your limit; he'll always be there to help you come through it.

1 CORINTHIANS 10:13 (*The Message*)

This is the Bible reading you heard in the session. You may have written it on to a small piece of card. (If not, you may like to do so.) Carry the card with you and read the Bible verse every now and then.

Use this space to write a prayer to God. (It may be something to do with your 'Try it!' placement.)

Use the space below to write, doodle or stick pictures about your thoughts and feelings while you are on your placement. How does the experience make you feel about God, about yourself and about others? (Don't forget to use the colour wheel if it helps you.) Also think about what you may like to try next!